YOUR **SKIN** FACTORY

CW00820203

SKIN ANALYSIS

LISTEN

LOOK

TOUCH

MACHINES

A Practical Guide

By Dr Des Fernandes MB, BCH, FRCS (Edin) *& Jennifer Munro*

Fernro Publishers Ltd. 2019

All rights reserved. No reproduction, copy or transmission of this publication may be made without written permission. No paragraph of this publication may be reproduced, copied, or transmitted save with the written permission or in accordance with the provisions of the Copyright, Designs and Patents Act 1988, or under the terms of any licence permitting limited copying issued by the Copyright Licensing Agency.

Any person who does any unauthorized act in relation to this publication may be liable to criminal prosecution and civil claims for damages. The authors have asserted their rights to be identified as the authors of this work in accordance with the Copyright, Designs and Patents Act 1988.

First published February 2019
Fernro Publishing Ltd.
London, United Kingdom

ISBN 978-1-9160348-8-4

Credits:
Valerie Carstens, Linda Jackson, and Carol and Rob Trow
for their help with proofreading.

Linda Jackson for her help with the development of the Questionnaire.

Kim Benvenuto for design and artwork.

Ernst Eiselen for the photography section.

This book is sold subject to the condition that it shall not, by way of trade or otherwise, be lent, re-sold, hired out, or otherwise circulated without the publisher's prior consent in any form of binding or cover other than that in which it is published, and without a similar condition including this condition being imposed on the subsequent purchaser.

www.fernro.com

www.skinscienceauthority.com

SKIN ANALYSIS
A Practical Guide

Sophisticated Information
Simple Delivery

By Dr Des Fernandes MB, BCH, FRCS (Edin)
& Jennifer Munro

CONTENTS

INTRODUCTION

Complex and scientific textbooks are available, but they make skin analysis very difficult to understand. This **simple book** is for therapists who really want to make a difference to their clients' skin. It is **not a scientific textbook for treating skin**, but will give you some of the insight you need to become an effective and sought-after skin care professional.

We've written three other books, with two other authors, Dr Ernst Eiselen and Dr Matthias Aust, that might help you to **deepen your knowledge** of our **unique way of looking at the skin**. They're all available from **www.yourskinfactory.com**. Think about getting these books for your customers or selling them through your business. Working with a **well-informed client** will help you to **build a long-term relationship** with that client, and thereby to build a **more stable and successful business.**

Dr Des Fernandes & Jennifer Munro

WELCOME TO THE
SKIN ANALYSIS FUNNEL

3 SKIN GROUPS

5 SKIN TYPES

7 SKIN CONDITIONS

INTERPRETATION

ACTION PLAN
Ingredients and treatments selector

WHY SHOULD WE ANALYSE SKIN?

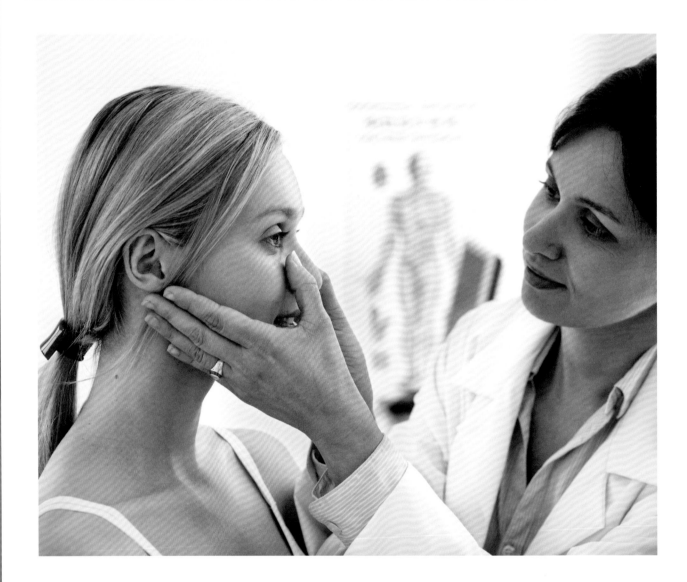

The Skin Analysis is the point at which you **start to bond** with your **new client**, and make them **feel they are listened to** and that they have your **complete attention**.

LISTEN AS CAREFULLY AS YOU CAN; YOUR CLIENT IS GIVING YOU THE DIAGNOSIS.

Skin analysis **builds loyalty** and **trust** as the Action Plan is carried out.

WE ALL HAVE DIFFERENT SKIN

This book is designed to help you to identify your clients'...

SKIN GROUP

SKIN TYPE

SKIN CONDITIONS

INTERPRETATION

3

Then you can suggest...

ACTION PLANS

**to remedy any shortcomings, and
maintain a healthy looking skin.**

When you work with a new client **record the starting point** so
that you can **see progress**, and **adjust the Action Plan** if necessary.

HOW TO USE THIS BOOK

We suggest you read **the whole book** through first.

Then visit **www.skinscienceauthority.com** and **register** using the **registration number** you will find on the **back cover** of your book.

Free membership will allow you to **download** all of the **documents you need** as well as many interesting **scientific papers** written by **Dr Des Fernandes**

When you have a client to see, **print** off a **Questionnaire**, an **Interpretation Chart** and the **Action Plan**.

Start with the **Questionnaire**.

Go through the Questionnaire **slowly and carefully**. Answer all the questions. This will give you a very good idea of **how your client views their own skin**.

Make **notes**.

Take your photographs as per the instructions.
* Remember to label the photographs properly – name and date.

STEP 6

YOU ARE NOW ENTERING YOUR SKIN ANALYSIS FUNNEL...

Level 1 – Select your client's Skin Group

Level 2 – Select your client's Skin Type

Level 3 – Determine your client's Skin Conditions

Refer to the sections Skin Groups, Skin Types and Skin Conditions to remind yourself of what certain things look like and to reassure yourself that you have identified them correctly – **don't forget to show your client**.

Level 4 – Interpretation:

Select the appropriate Skin Group Interpretation chart, and then put your ticks/notes in the right boxes.

Level 5 – Develop an Action Plan.

Now that you know exactly what Group, Type and Conditions you're looking at, you are empowered to work out the best Action Plan from the Ingredients and Treatments Selector.

STEP 7

Attach the **Questionnaire**, the **Interpretation Chart**, the **Photographs** and the **Action Plan** together to form your **Client Record Card**.

HOW TO USE THIS QUESTIONNAIRE

The questionnaire is designed to help you to find out…

1. PERSONAL DETAILS

What are you going to do with the information?

You are going to create a confidential **client record card**.

Why?

So that every time your client comes to see you, you are fully **aware** of **everything that has gone before** and what your **objectives** are for this person.

2. WHAT ARE YOUR MAIN AREAS OF CONCERN?

What are you going to do with the information?

Bear it in mind so that you make sure that this is the one thing you **seek a solution** for before anything else.

Why?

To **build trust** and **loyalty** with your client and make them feel **listened to**.

3. HEREDITARY HISTORY

What are you going to do with the information?

Be aware that your client may be **more at risk** from certain conditions than others, and that their **genetic make-up** may be the **reason they have a condition** rather than anything they are doing or not doing.

Why?

You can make a more **informed Analysis** and **realistic Action Plan**.

4. LIFESTYLE

What are you going to do with the information?

Offer advice on **health improvement** and the **effect** that it will have **on the skin**.

Why?

So that you can **improve** the likelihood of success for your Action Plan.

5. CURRENT SKIN CARE

What are you going to do with the information?

You are going to learn about your **client's skin care regimen**.

Why?

So that you will be able to **judge the possible cause of any problems** or **see what has worked well in the past**.

6. MEDICATIONS

What are you going to do with the information?

You are going to learn about your **client's health**.

Why?

So that you will be aware of any of the **potential causes** of skin problems or past improvements **due to medication**, and so that you will be aware of any areas **where you should exercise caution** in your treatments.

7. MEDICAL CONDITIONS

What are you going to do with the information?

Each **medical condition** will **indicate something** that you need to be **aware of** when you treat this client or recommend something for them.

Why?

This is for **safety reasons.** For example: Claustrophobia may mean that your client will not enjoy a mask over their face. Epilepsy may mean that they should not have electrical treatments, and you should know what to do if they have a seizure while you are treating them. **Allergies** will mean that you must **check your ingredients** carefully and eczema will allow ingredients to be more efficiently absorbed through the skin, increasing the risk of a **Retinoid Reaction**.

8. PREVIOUS COSMETIC TREATMENTS

What are you going to do with the information?

Many cosmetic treatments are **harmful to the skin.** For example: you need to understand that you may be looking at dryness caused by microdermabrasion or laser treatment and not a Dry Skin Type.

Why?

So that you can **design a treatment plan** that will repair the effects of damage and normalise the appearance of the skin.

9. SKIN GROUPS

What are you going to do with the information?

Choose a **Sunsense Programme** for your client.

Why?

Protect the skin from the sun appropriately in a sensible way.

10. SKIN TYPES

What are you going to do with the information?

Design a **daily** regimen as well as any specialised treatments.

Why?

Maintain the skin to be as **healthy-looking** as it can be.

11. SKIN CONDITIONS

What are you going to do with the information?

Recommend a **specific** daily regimen and possible intensive professional care for the condition.

Why?

Improve the effects of their conditions over time.

12. SPECIAL CAUTIONS

What are you going to do with the information?

Take note that your client may have some requirements due to a condition or a phobia.

Why?

To ensure your client's comfort and safety at all times.

SKIN ZONES

You should use these simple charts to guide you in your analysis of the face.

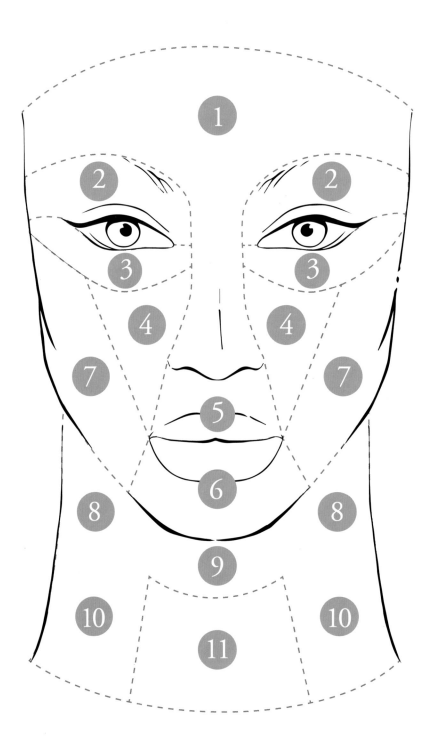

COMMON FEATURES TO LOOK FOR ARE:

1. **T zone, whole forehead and nose** – oiliness, enlarged pores, sebaceous gland hyperplasia.

2. **Upper eyelids and temples** – photo-ageing showing as lines and wrinkles

3. **Lower eyelids** – fine wrinkles of photo-ageing, dynamic crow's feet wrinkles

4. **Central cheeks** – Melasma, fine laxity wrinkles of photo-ageing, rosacea and dilated pores

5. **Upper lip** – wrinkles resulting from loss of volume

6. **Lower lip and chin** – loss of volume, lines and pitting of chin, dilated pores and rosacea

7. **Cheeks in front of ear** – pigmentation marks, vertical wrinkles in front of ears from photo-damage.

8, 9, 10. **Neck and sides of neck** – photo-damage, elastosis, poikiloderma, pale patch under the chin.

11. **Central lower neck** – elastosis, collagen loss causing skin laxity, photo-ageing

SOME GENERAL ADVICE

1. **Greet** your clients **warmly** to make them feel **relaxed** and **comfortable**.

2. Be **culturally sensitive**, as some cultures require a **wide personal space** – a **firm handshake** may be best.

3. Always remember to **make eye contact** with your client.

4. Always **sit opposite your client**, in a **well-lit room. Do not ask your client to lie down.** This is so that you will be able to see the **full extent** of the issues including **how the skin 'hangs'** on the face.

5. Have a **good hand mirror** with you that your client can show you the areas of concern and you can point out relevant issues.

6. Try to **be** as **detailed** in your observation as possible.

7. **Don't be afraid** to **give your opinion** – that's why your client is with you!

8. **Be honest** and **down to earth** – never use technical language if **simple words** will do.

9. When you are both at ease, **begin** with the **Questionnaire** supplied.

Look out for Dr Des's advice as you go though the Questionnaire and the rest of this book. It will always look like this speech bubble.

12

CONFIDENTIAL QUESTIONNAIRE

 Go to www.skinscienceauthority.com to download your free copy of this questionnaire.

I. PERSONAL DETAILS

Today's Date:

First Name: Last Name:

Date of Birth: Occupation:

Address:

Phone:

 Home: Work: Mobile:

Email address: Doctor:

Referred by:

○ Friend (name):   ○ Gift Voucher:

○ Website: ○ Other:

2. WHAT ARE YOUR MAIN AREAS OF CONCERN?

WHAT HAVE YOU DONE ABOUT THIS SO FAR?

> You need to know if your client has any pre-existing conditions and how they assess their own skin's condition. Let them fill in the boxes but you should also modify the notes when necessary.

3. HEREDITARY HISTORY

DESCRIBE ANY RELEVANT HEREDITARY HISTORY YOU MAY HAVE

If the client has a problem we need to know if this runs in their family.

ANY FAMILY HISTORY OF SKIN CANCER?

○ Yes

○ No

One should be aware of melanoma. No pigmented area should be treated on customers with a family history of melanoma, but should be referred to their doctor.

4. LIFESTYLE

HOW WOULD YOU DESCRIBE YOUR OVERALL HEALTH?

○ Excellent   ○ Good   ○ Fair   ○ Moderate   ○ Poor

DO YOU TAKE VITAMINS, MINERALS OR PROTEIN SUPPLEMENTS?

Which?   Dose?

DO YOU SMOKE?

How many years have you been smoking?   How much per day?

IS YOUR STRESS LEVEL:

○ High   ○ Medium   ○ Low

This may help explain resistant acne.

DO YOU NORMALLY SLEEP WELL?

○ Yes   ○ No

DIET AND EXERCISE

	Healthy answer	Unhealthy answer
Do you exercise regularly?	○ Yes	○ No
Do you follow a fat-free diet?	○ No	○ Yes
Do you follow a low carb diet with normal/high fat?	○ No	○ Yes
Do you restrict sugar in your diet?	○ Yes	○ No
Do you have a high protein diet?	○ No	○ Yes
How many glasses of liquid do you consume daily? e.g. water	○ 2+ glasses	○ 1 glass
How many cups of caffeinated TEA do you consume daily?	○ 1-3 cups	○ 4+ cups

People worry that this may cause dry skin, but I think that it is not likely.

	Healthy answer	Unhealthy answer
How many cups of caffeinated COFFEE do you consume daily?	○ 1-3 cups	○ 4+ cups

People worry that this may cause dry skin, but I think that it is not likely.

Are you a Vegetarian?	○ Yes	○ No

Check for protein deficiency causing collagen loss and vitamin B12 deficiency.

Are you a Vegan?	○ Yes	○ No

Check for protein deficiency causing collagen loss and vitamin B12 deficiency.

5. CURRENT SKIN CARE

WHAT IS YOUR PRESENT SKIN REGIMEN?

○ Soap & water only   Brand/type:

○ Cleanser   Brand/type:

○ Toner   Brand/type:

○ Moisturiser   Brand/type:

○ Mask   Brand/type:

○ Exfoliation   Brand/type:

○ Sunblock every day   Brand/type:

○ Other   Brand/type:

16

6. MEDICATIONS

WHAT MEDICATIONS/HORMONE REPLACEMENTS ARE YOU TAKING?

> Hormonal treatments may be associated with pigmentation problems so always ask if problems were related to hormone therapy.

HAVE YOU EVER USED...

○ Roaccutane / Cis-retinoic acid?

When did you start?

When did you finish?

> General indication of acne. Treat people very carefully if they are on high dose Roaccutane. If the client was on a high dose, avoid any vigorous treatments for about 6 months.

○ Differin Gel / Adapalene?

When did you start?

When did you finish?

> Used for acne.

HAVE YOU EVER USED (CONTD)...

○ Topical Antibiotics?

When did you start?

When did you finish?

___

○ Anti-fungal nail treatments?

When did you start?

When did you finish?

___

○ Topical Cortisone?

When did you start?

When did you finish?

7. MEDICAL CONDITIONS

HAVE YOU EVER HAD ANY OF THE FOLLOWING?

○ Fever blisters / cold sores / herpes

○ Yes   ○ No

> We need to be aware that certain treatments, like peeling, may exacerbate herpes.

___

○ Acne

Since when?   Where on your body?

> Be aware of relevant severity.

___

○ Allergies e.g. Salicylates, sunscreens, antibiotics etc.

Since when?   Describe symptoms and area of the body affected

___

○ Claustrophobia

Since when?   If yes, would a mask disturb you?

> This is important if you intend to suggest masks in treatment.

___

○ Diabetes

○ Type 1   ○ Type 2

> Type 1 usually starts in youth. Type 2 is associated with metabolic syndrome.

HAVE YOU EVER HAD ANY OF THE FOLLOWING? (contd.)

○ Eczema

Since when?　　What type or where in your body?

This lets you know to be careful and concentrate on antioxidant and vitamin A treatments.

○ Epilepsy

Since when?　　What type and describe warning signs?

May be exacerbated by electrical currents.

○ Joint replacement

Since when?　　What type or where in your body?

May cause discomfort if iontophoresis is done.

○ Heart disease / conditions

Since when?　　What type?

○ Pacemaker or valve replacement

Since when?

This is a contra-indication to electrical treatments.

○ Metal implants

Since when?　　What type or where in your body?

May make galvanic treatments uncomfortable.

○ Menopause/peri-menopausal states

When did it start?

May indicate hormonal changes.

○ Hepatitis

Since when?　　What type?

Do you take oral contraceptives?

This may show as acne, pigmentation and blemishes.

○ Yes　　　　○ No

Are you pregnant, or trying to get pregnant?

○ Yes   ○ No

> *This is generally a contra-indication to machine treatments. Light peels are allowed.*

Do you experience hormone imbalances?   ○ Yes   ○ No

Do you wear contact lenses?

○ Yes   ○ No

> *This is just a precaution. Some people prefer to remove contact lenses with treatments.*

HAVE YOU EVER HAD A REACTION TO...

○ Cosmetics   ○ Metals   ○ Medication   ○ Food

○ Fragrance   ○ Airborne particles   ○ Unidentified substance

8. PREVIOUS COSMETIC TREATMENTS

HAVE YOU EVER HAD...

○ Peels?

How recently & type:

> *Deep peels may contribute to skin problems.*

○ Microdermabrasion or Dermablading?

How recently & type:

> *This may be the cause of many problems – sensitivity, dryness, wrinkling etc.*

○ Injectables?

How recently & type:

○ Botulinum Toxin?

How recently & type:

HAVE YOU EVER HAD... (contd.)

○ Cosmetic surgery?

How recently & type:

○ Laser/ablative resurfacing, partially ablative/non-ablative?

How recently & type:

This may be the cause of many problems – sensitivity, dryness, wrinkling etc.

○ Skin Needling?

By needle length:

○ Other relevant procedures?

How recently & type:

○ Hydroquinone?

When did you start?

When did you finish?

Used for pigmentation, and if pigmentation recurs it tends to be difficult to treat.

○ Retin-A/ Retinoic acid or Tretinoin?

When did you start?

When did you finish?

Used for acne and photo-ageing.

○ Alpha Hydroxy Acids?

When did you start?

When did you finish?

9. SKIN GROUPS

GROUP A

○ **Sun sensitive**
Always burns and/or blisters – or burns easily but either never tans or only slightly.
Fitzpatrick I and II

GROUP B

○ **Sun tolerant**
Seldom burns and shows a moderate to good tan.
Fitzpatrick III and IV

GROUP C

○ **Sun Resistant**
Never burns and shows a deep tan.
Fitzpatrick V and VI

DO YOU HAVE THE GENE FOR "RED-HAIR"?

○ Yes

○ No

> The reason we ask this is that these people generally have very sun-sensitive skin and may also be prone to developing malignant melanoma.

10. SKIN TYPES

HOW WOULD YOU DESCRIBE YOUR SKIN?

○ Normal   ○ Dry   ○ Oily

○ Combination   ○ Red / Sensitive

DO YOU EVER EXPERIENCE...

○ Flakiness or scaly skin?

> *This generally indicates dry skin and vitamin A depletion.*

○ Tightness?

> *This generally indicates sensitive skin.*

○ Redness?

> *This may indicate sensitive skin or rosacea or other inflammatory conditions.*

○ Excessive oily shine during the day?

> *This will indicate oily skin that may be prone to acne or break-outs.*

DO YOU BLUSH EASILY?

○ Yes   ○ No

> *This tells us if the client's skin will tend to be sensitive and redder than people who don't blush easily.*

DUE TO...

○ Emotions   ○ Foods   ○ Temperature change   ○ Other

11. SKIN CONDITIONS

SKIN PROBLEMS?

○ Ageing   ○ Fine lines & wrinkles   ○ Dryness

○ Acne   ○ Pigmentation   ○ Scars

○ Skin cancer   ○ Eczema, rashes, allergies

Other? Describe...

DOES YOUR SKIN...

○ Heal quickly?   ○ Scar?   ○ Pigment easily

ARE YOU UNDER TREATMENT FOR CURRENT SKIN CONDITIONS?

○ Yes

If yes, what?

○ No

DO YOU...

○ Sun bathe   ○ Use a tanning bed?

> Using a sunbed predisposes the skin to photo-ageing, pigmentation problems, keratosis and skin cancers.

Sun tan history:

12. SPECIAL CAUTIONS

DO YOU...

Have any phobias?

> This is important to know.
> For example, a customer may not like a mask on their face.

Have any preferences we should know about?

> Once the skin analysis has been done, tell the client the following...

In our treatment program, it may be necessary to recommend alterations and/or additions to your home care regimen. We will recommend the appropriate schedule for future facial treatments or referral in order to achieve your skin improvement goals.

Client signature   Date

TOOL 1

LISTEN

WHAT ARE YOU LISTENING FOR?

First **find out** what **concerns your clients MOST** about their skin.
It will be the **reason** they came to see you.

Always ask the following:

| What concerns you most? | When did it start? | What steps have you taken so far? |

| What else concerns you about your skin? | How did it start? | What steps have you taken so far? |

YOU ARE LISTENING FOR

> All the clues are here. Your client will give them to you.

> Discuss the answers in depth.
> Be a detective.
> Remember your training.

FOR EXAMPLE:

Your client says: "I love sunbathing. Every year I go on holiday in the sun."

You know: Photo damage is inevitable –> Make a note.

Your client says: "My skin is dry and flaky, so I exfoliate regularly."

You know: Your client is damaging her skin and exposing it to risk –> Make a note.

Your client says: "My parent had skin cancer."

You know: Your client may be at risk too –> Make a note.

TOOL 2

LOOK

◎ First **remove** any **make-up** or ask your client not to wear any.

◎ By looking, you can gain some **valuable clues** to your client's **Skin Group** and **Skin Type** as you will find out later on.

◎ **Skin Conditions** are often immediately apparent if you **look carefully**.

◎ Remember to ask your client to **sit opposite** you, **AND NOT LIE DOWN,** for a skin analysis so that you can see how the **skin hangs** on the face.

◎ You can use a **magnifying light** to see some of the **finer clues** such as fine **lines and wrinkles**.

◎ Try to be as **detailed** in your **observation** as possible.

YOU WILL BE LOOKING FOR

COLOUR

Look for the **basic skin colour** because that will give you an idea of the client's **risks for photo-damage**: the lighter the colour the greater the chance for **photo-damage**. Freckles always indicate photo-damage. Look for **irregularities of colour.**

TEXTURE & SURFACE

Look for **flaky dry** skin, look at the cheeks and the nose to see **enlarged pores**, look for any **surface irregularities** that may mean you should refer your client to a doctor. Look for **fine wrinkles** that may indicate **dry skin** or **photo-damage** or **volume loss in the face**.

DEEP STRUCTURE

Clues to the **deep structure** of the skin (**collagen and elastin issues**). Can you see **lax**, **wrinkled skin** that indicates **photo-damage** or **stretch marks?**

SKIN CONDITIONS

Most people have **photo-damage**. Of course you will see **acne**, and **scars** etc. easily. It may be difficult to see that the **redness** of the cheeks is actually **rosacea. Pigmented blotches** on the cheeks and temples, pigmentation around the mouth or on the forehead may indicate **melasma**.

TOOL 3

TOUCH

Touching your client's skin is the **next step** in the **process**.

Remember that this is sometimes a **very sensitive thing** for a person with a **skin problem**.

Be **conscious** of your client's preferences.

You **cannot** do this with **gloves on** – make sure your hands are **hygienically cleaned** immediately before touching any client.

What you **feel though your fingertips** will give you a lot of **information**.

Always be **gentle.**

WHAT CAN TOUCHING
TELL YOU?

If the skin is oily or dry.

If it has good elasticity. Gently pull the skin
to judge its recoil. Does it snap back quickly
or does it take some time?

Whether or not it has a good blood supply.
Press on the skin to see how quickly the
blood returns. Are there any dilated vessels
on the surface?

If the surface skin is well-attached to the deeper
skin. Pinch the skin gently, and see if it lifts away
from the deeper structure.

If there are any nodular areas indicating obstruction
or retention of sebaceous glands. Feel for unusual
lumps or bumps.

MACHINES

In general, most client's Skin Conditions can be analysed without diagnostic machines, but machines can be used to confirm a diagnosis. **Photo-ageing**, however is **straightforward to diagnose**, but with machines, we can often **quantify** the **degree of damage** and then **monitor the progress**.

WOOD'S LAMP (Filtered UV light rays around 365nm) is very useful and reveals things like **superficial pigmentation**, **porphyrins**, **fungal conditions**, **depth of pigmentation** and **vascular disorders** that cannot be seen with the naked eye. The best units photograph and transfer for storage.

- **Normal skin** is **light blue-grey**.

- **Solar induced epidermal pigmentation** tends to be **dark**, **superficial** and **sharply defined**. It shows up well with a Wood's Lamp.

- **Dermal pigmentation**, on the other hand, is **shadowy** (almost undetectable).

- **Keratoses** or **thickened stratum corneum** will show up **white**.

- **Oily** areas will be **yellow**.

- **Vitiligo** will **fluoresce blue-white**.

- **Porphyrins** will be **pink-red** and can show up as little spots in acne from the porphyrins in the p.acnes (bacteria).

USE WOODS LAMP TO REVEAL UNDERLYING DAMAGE

Normal light shows less evidence of damage

Black light shows underlying problems

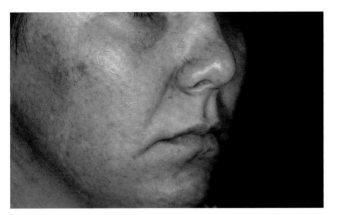 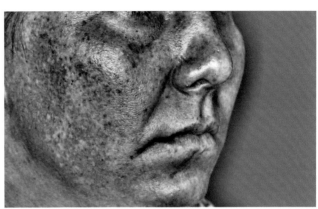

USE A WOOD'S LAMP AS FOLLOWS:

Skin to be examined should not have been washed in the past half hour or had any make-up, deodorant, sunscreen or moisturising cream applied, as these can show as fluorescence, causing a false positive result.

Gentle facial skin cleansing may be required.

Follow the advice of the Wood's Lamp manufacturer.

OTHER MACHINES

Other machines can give you the following information:

⚙ Elasticity by estimating recoil after negative pressure suction.

⚙ Hydration is done indirectly by measuring surface oils.

⚙ Sebum secretion.

⚙ Colour of pigmented marks. It is extremely difficult to do precise measurements.

⚙ Relief impressions of skin surface. This also should be done in extremely controlled situations. If you use Alginate masks for treatment, then consider keeping a selected area of the eyes or the upper lip that show wrinkles. This can be dried and then used for a comparison after a course of treatments.

PHOTOGRAPHY

With thanks to Dr. Ernst Eiselen

1   WHY SHOULD YOU TAKE PHOTOGRAPHS?

Improvements in skin **take** some **time** to show.

Clients can't always **remember** what they looked like.

They often **seek perfection** and **get upset** when it **doesn't happen immediately**.

Photographs show them **how far** they've come and **encourage them** to **keep the treatment up**.

You need to be sure you are on the **right track** too.

Comparisons are the way forward!

2   WHY YOU SHOULD GET PERMISSION FROM YOUR CLIENT

It may be the law where you live.

If you have permission, you can show other clients the photographs in order to **prove that you are doing good work**, and the **products** you recommend are **effective**.

You can use the photographs to **train new staff**.

You too can **learn a lot** from a visual record.

Any camera that gives you **2 megapixels** or more will create **great images**.

Invest in **good software** that allows you to **store the images**, create albums, and edit out distinguishing features (like eyes) if you are going to show the pictures to others. These photographs are your **verification** and your **treasure**.

These days, some **smart phones** have **good** enough **cameras**.

It's important to always take the pictures from the **same distance away** from your subject. Use a **dedicated chair**, a **mark on the floor** and a **tripod** for this. Tripods mean that your **hand shaking** won't affect the pictures.

Invest in a **photographer's lamp** and **position** it in the **same way** every time. If possible, **block out natural light** from the room.

Keep hairbands and clips nearby so you can **keep** the **client's hair off their face**. Always do the same on follow-up photos.

A plain background. These can be bought from photographer's stores, or if you have a dedicated area for photography, make sure the wall behind is plain and neutral. Dark or grey backgrounds are best. It is essential to take photos in the **same place** every time.

SOME HANDY TIPS

1   Keep a **constant** and **plain background**.
Make sure the background is always **clean**.

2   Always take **six pictures** of a face – one set with the **flash on** – full frontal, left side, right side and one set with the **flash off**. Taking pictures with the flash off gives a more **realistic image**.

3   Remove all jewellery and make-up.

4   Clip a **dark cloth** around your subject's neck so that their **clothing colour** will **not affect** the photograph.

5   Make sure that your **camera settings** are **always the same**.

6   Try to set your camera so that you get at least a **500kb JPEG image**. This will allow you to zoom in to the picture for close ups of problem areas. 500kb can be emailed easily.

5

FLASH ON

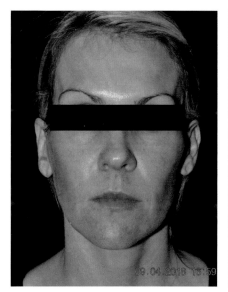 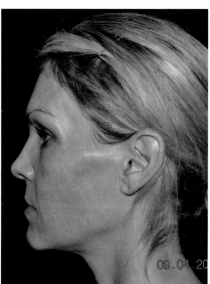 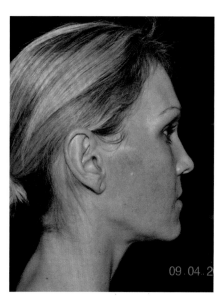

| **Full frontal** | **Left side** | **Right side** |

FLASH OFF

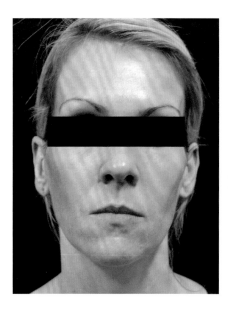 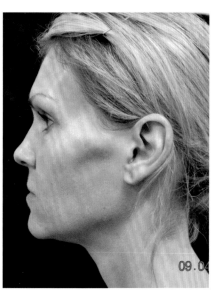 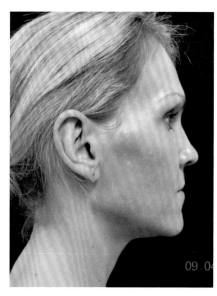

| **Full frontal** | **Left side** | **Right side** |

YOU'RE NOW READY TO ENTER:

THE SKIN ANALYSIS FUNNEL

YOUR TOOLS

  LISTEN
 LOOK

 TOUCH MACHINES
 LOOK
LISTEN

TOUCH MACHINES
LOOK
LISTEN

3 SKIN GROUPS

GROUP **A** GROUP **B** **C** GROUP

LEVEL 1

5 SKIN TYPES

 NORMAL SKIN
 COMBINATION SKIN
 DRY SKIN
 OILY SKIN
RED / SENSITIVE SKIN

LEVEL 2

7 SKIN CONDITIONS

1 2 3 4 5 6 7

LEVEL 3

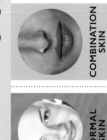
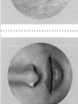

INTERPRETATION

+ **YOUR TRAINING AS A THERAPIST**

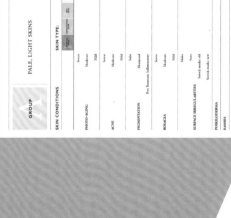

ACTION PLAN

Ingredients and treatments selector

+ **YOUR PRODUCT AND TREATMENT KNOWLEDGE**

LEVEL 4

LEVEL 5

LEVEL 1

3 SKIN GROUPS

5 SKIN TYPES

7 SKIN CONDITIONS

INTERPRETATION

ACTION PLAN
Ingredients and treatments selector

SKIN GROUPS

- What is the **natural ethnic colour** of the skin?

- The **Fitzpatrick scale** is a tool that places everyone into one of six groups. We believe it can be made **simpler**, because what we are really trying to do, is **estimate the risk** to the skin of **sun damage**.

- In our **grading system** we only use **3 grades** because it is **easier to place** people in these three groups.

 Sensitive to light

 **More tolerant of light**

 **More resistant to light**

- The general rule is that the **lighter the skin and eyes**, the **more at risk** the skin is.

- Which group would your client belong to?

- Use two of your **four tools** to **determine a Skin Group**.

GROUP **A**

This group has the **greatest risk** from **sun damage and skin cancer.**

LISTEN

Your client will tell you that they **cannot stay in the sun** for **any length of time** without **burning**. They will **blister** and **peel** and either **cannot tan** at all, or only slightly. They may tell you that their ethnic background is **Celtic**, **Scandinavian** or at least **Northern European**.

Many Scandinavians are more sun-tolerant than Scots and pale-skinned Dutch people, and many East Asians are very susceptible to sun damage too.

LOOK

Your client will have **pale skin**, **blue or light green eyes** and **red** or **pale blonde hair**. They may have some signs of **photo-ageing** such as **brown spots**, **wrinkles** and **freckles**.

GROUP B

This group has a **moderate risk of sun damage** and **skin cancer.**

LISTEN

Your client will tell you that they can **stay in the sun for some time** without burning. They will only **blister** and **peel** if they stay for a **longer time without sun protection**. This group **tans easily**. They may tell you that their ethnic background is **Mediterranean, Southern European, Middle Eastern, Indian, Far Eastern** or a **combination of any race.**

LOOK

Your client will have **light brown skin**, **brown eyes** and **brown hair**. They generally have **fewer signs of fine wrinkles** than in Group A, but can have **freckles and brown spots** or larger areas of pigmentation such as **Melasma**.

C GROUP

This group has the **least risk of sun damage and skin cancer.**

LISTEN

Your client will tell you that they can **stay in the sun for greater lengths of time** without burning. They will **never blister** and **peel**. They will most likely tell you that their **ethnic background** is **African** or **Indian**.

LOOK

Your client will have **very dark skin**, **dark black** or **brown eyes** and **black hair**. They can have **pigmentation problems**. **Wrinkles** only tend to appear **late in life**.

3 SKIN GROUPS

5 SKIN TYPES

7 SKIN CONDITIONS

INTERPRETATION

ACTION PLAN
Ingredients and treatments selector

SKIN TYPES

We identify **five Skin Types**.
Use your **four tools** to find out which **Skin Type** your client has.

NORMAL SKIN

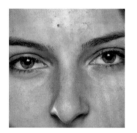

COMBINATION SKIN

DRY SKIN

OILY SKIN

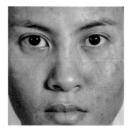

RED / SENSITIVE SKIN

LISTEN

If your client **doesn't complain** about **greasy skin** or **oily skin**, or if he or she has no real complaints, the **chances are** they have **normal skin.**

LOOK

You won't see many **imperfections** at all. The **pores** will be **barely visible**. The **complexion** will be **youthful** and **radiant**. There will be **no** fine or deep **wrinkles** and **no** patches of **red sensitivity**.

TOUCH

You will **not feel** any **unusual lumps** or **bumps**. The skin will feel **smooth, elastic** and **well-moisturised**. The texture will be **fine** and **firm.**

MACHINES

The Wood's Lamp will show that most of the skin is **light blue-grey**.

46

COMBINATION SKIN

 **LISTEN**

This is a very **common Skin Type** so don't be surprised to hear your client say she has **dry** or **normal** skin on her **cheeks** and an **oily T zone**.

 **LOOK**

You will see **greasy**, **shiny skin** with **open pores** on the nose, forehead and chin. There may even be **pimples**. The cheeks may have **fine wrinkles** or be **smooth**.

47

 **TOUCH**

Just like the tests for dry and oily skin, you will feel with your fingers that the **T zone is oily** and the **side areas are dry or normal**. It is important to realise that the **changes** may be **subtle**.

 **MACHINES**

The Wood's Lamp will show large areas of **purple** or **light grey-blue** for the cheeks and **yellow** for the T zone.

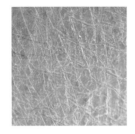

DRY SKIN

 **LISTEN**

Your client is likely to say that their **skin feels taut**, **tight** and **rough**. They may complain of **flakiness** and **wrinkles**. The skin may **swing** from **oily to dry** and **back again**. The skin may be **sore** and **uncomfortable**.

 **LOOK**

You will see **fine wrinkles** around the eyes and on the cheeks. The skin will appear **whitish and flaky**. The skin will be **dull** and sometimes **grey**.

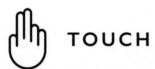 **TOUCH**

Take the skin of the cheeks between your fingers and gently bring your fingers together. This may reveal **fine wrinkles**. The skin will feel **rough rather than smooth**.

 **MACHINES**

The Wood's Lamp will show **large areas of purple** and some **light grey-white patches**.

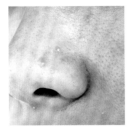

OILY SKIN

 **LISTEN**

Your client is likely to say that their **skin feels greasy**. They may **dislike creams** because they think creams make the skin greasier. They generally **hate** the idea of **using** an **oil preparation**. They may complain about **break-outs**, **open pores** and **shine**.

 **LOOK**

You will often see **enlarged pores**, congested areas of **blackheads** are not uncommon, and **whiteheads** and even **acne pustules** may be present. The **skin will shine**, and it may appear **thickened** or **dull**.

 **TOUCH**

Your **fingertips** will feel **oily**, and there will most likely be **lumps** and **bumps** under the skin due to **blocked sebaceous glands**.

 **MACHINES**

The Wood's Lamp will show large areas of **yellow**. Porphyrins will be **pink-red** and can show up as little spots in acne from the porphyrins in the p.acnes (bacteria).

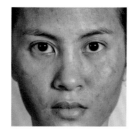

RED / SENSITIVE SKIN

 **LISTEN**

Clients with **sensitive skin** will usually tell you that there are a wide range of **cosmetics** that they can't use because they **burn** or make them **itch**. Their skin may even burn and itch without the presence of cosmetics.

 **LOOK**

You will see **red patches** or blotches, usually on the **cheeks**. There may be areas of **dryness** and **itchiness**. There may even be **rashes** on the eyelids. The skin may appear **fragile**.

 **TOUCH**

The skin may feel **rough** as the sensitivity has caused **peeling**. It may even seem **thin**.

 **MACHINES**

Sensitive skin is often dry, so the Wood's Lamp will show large areas of **purple**.

51

3 SKIN GROUPS

5 SKIN TYPES

LEVEL 3

7 SKIN CONDITIONS

INTERPRETATION

ACTION PLAN
Ingredients and treatments selector

SKIN CONDITIONS

Now you can use your **four tools** to determine which Skin Conditions **exist**, and are **relevant**.

1   PHOTO-AGEING

2   ACNE

3   PIGMENTATION

4   ROSACEA

5   SURFACE IRREGULARITIES

6   POIKILODERMA OF CIVATTE

7   RASHES

1

PHOTO-AGEING – MILD

LISTEN

Your client will say that they have been **exposed to the sun**.

LOOK

Freckles on cheeks, nose and arms

Few **pigmentary blemishes**

TOUCH

You will be unlikely to feel any **irregularity**.

MACHINES

Solar induced epidermal pigmentation tends to be **dark, superficial** and **sharply defined** on the Wood's Lamp, and it shows up well. Dermal pigmentation, on the other hand, is shadowy (almost undetectable).

PHOTO-AGEING – MODERATE

LISTEN

Your client will say that they have **wrinkles**, **brown spots**, **white lumps** in the skin of the neck, sagging skin.

LOOK

Freckles	**Smile lines**
Pigmentary blemishes	**Dry, ashen skin**
Fine wrinkles	**Uneven skin colour**

TOUCH

Loss of skin tone

Dryness

MACHINES

Solar induced epidermal pigmentation tends to be **dark, superficial** and **sharply defined** on the Wood's Lamp, and it shows up well. Dermal pigmentation, on the other hand, is shadowy (almost undetectable).

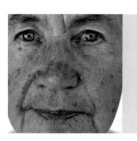

PHOTO-AGEING – SEVERE

LISTEN

Your client will say that they have **wrinkles, brown spots, white lumps** in the skin of the neck, **sagging skin, keratoses** and **solar lentigines**.

LOOK

Brown patches	Laxity
Deep static wrinkles	Keratosis
Easy bruising	Skin cancer
Elastosis	

TOUCH

Dry and rough

Poor circulation

Poor elastic recoil

MACHINES

Solar induced epidermal pigmentation tends to be **dark, superficial** and **sharply defined** on the Wood's Lamp, and it shows up well. **Dermal pigmentation**, on the other hand, is **shadowy** (almost undetectable). **Keratoses** or **thickened stratum corneum** will show up **white**.

56

2

ACNE – MODERATE

LISTEN

Your client will say that they are embarrassed by **pimples**, worried about **scars**.

LOOK

Blackheads	**Pimples**
Whiteheads	**Mild inflammation**
Greasy T Zone	

TOUCH

Be **very sensitive** about **touching** this kind of skin. The skin may be **painful** and the client may feel **uncomfortable** with touch.

MACHINES

On the Wood's Lamp, Porphyrins will be **pink-red** and can show up as little spots from the porphyrins in the p.acnes (bacteria).

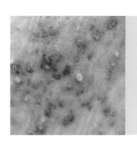

2

ACNE – SEVERE

LISTEN

Your client will say that they are embarrassed by **pimples**, worried about **scars**.

LOOK

Blackheads	Pimples
Whiteheads	Pus
Solar Comedones	Swollen nodules
Greasy T Zone	Blind cysts
Boils and abscesses	Scars

TOUCH

Loss of skin tone

Dry and rough

Thick, disordered stratum corneum

Poor circulation

Poor elastic recoil

MACHINES

On the Wood's Lamp, Porphyrins will be **pink-red** and can show up as little spots from the porphyrins in the p.acnes (bacteria).

3

LISTEN

When did the pigmentation occur? Was it after a bad **sunburn** or after a **hormonal change**?

LOOK

Brown marks, only in places that **catch the sun.**

MACHINES

Solar induced epidermal pigmentation tends to be dark, superficial and sharply defined on the Wood's Lamp, and it shows up well. Keratoses or thickened stratum corneum will show up **white**.

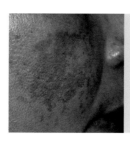

3

PIGMENTATION – HORMONAL MELASMA

LISTEN

When did the pigmentation occur? Was it after a bad **sunburn** or after a **hormonal change**?

LOOK

Can be anywhere on the body

Dark rings around the eyes

Especially in people with Group B skin

Pigmentation of the armpits, under the breasts and in the groin

MACHINES

Often does not show up.

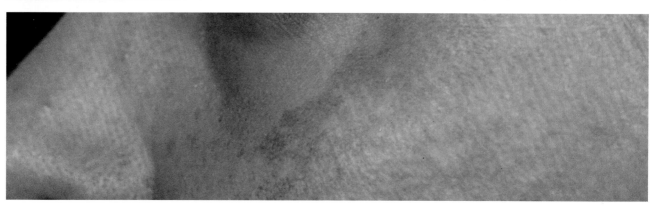

60

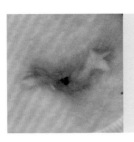

PIGMENTATION – POST-TRAUMATIC INFLAMMATORY

LISTEN

Your client will say that they have had an **accident** of some kind, or an **infection**.

LOOK

Brown, uneven pigmentation at the wound site.

TOUCH

You may feel a **rough surface.**

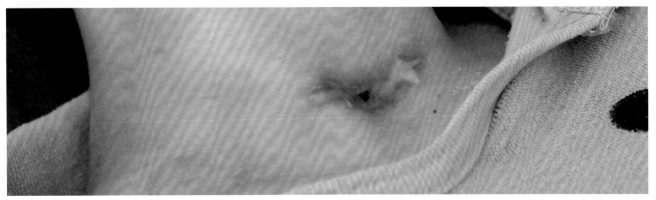

4

ROSACEA

LISTEN

Your client will complain that their skin is **red**, **sensitive** and **dry** on the **cheeks, nose, chin** and **between the eyebrows**.

Family history of rosacea.

Client may say it happens when they are **exposed to extremes** of temperature, eating **spicy food**, **exercise** or **alcohol**.

LOOK

Dryness	Usually in pale skin
Redness	Often in women
Swelling	Little pimples
Drinker's nose	

TOUCH

Swollen bumps in the red areas.

LISTEN

Your client may tell you that a mole has **changed in size**, **shape** or **colour** or that it has become **painful** or **itchy**. It may have started to **ooze**, **bleed** or **swell**. All of these are worrying signs and should be referred to a doctor.

Normal moles usually appear during childhood or young adulthood.

What does a normal mole look like?

Evenly coloured brown, tan, or black, flat or raised, round or oval and less than 6 mm across

What does an abnormal mole look like?

The A,B,C,D,E method:

LOOK

• **A is for Asymmetry:** One half of a mole or birthmark does not match the other.

• **B is for Border:** The edges are irregular, ragged, notched, or blurred.

• **C is for Colour:** The colour is not the same all over and may include different shades of brown or black, or sometimes with patches of pink, red, white, or blue.

• **D is for Diameter:** The spot is larger than 6 mm across.

• **E is for Evolving:** The mole is changing in size, shape, or colour.

N.B. Some melanomas don't fit these rules.

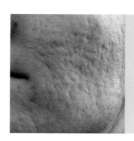

5

SURFACE IRREGULARITIES – SCARS

64

LISTEN

Your client will say that they have had **acne**. They may say that they suffered from **inflammation**, **pustules** and **painful lumps**.

LOOK

ACNE SCARS

• **Pitted** or **cobblestone** appearance.

TRAUMA SCARS

• Variety of different shaped scars from **cuts** and **burns**.

KELOID SCARS

• Thick, discoloured scars that **pull at the skin** and **get larger** over time.

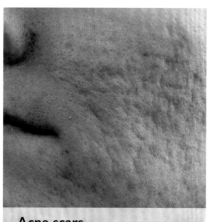

Acne scars

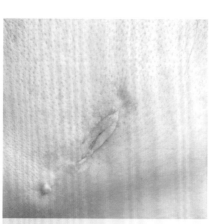

Trauma scars

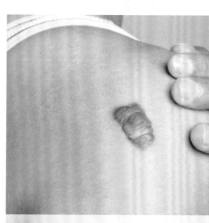

Keloid scars

SURFACE IRREGULARITIES – STRETCH MARKS

LISTEN

Your client will tell you that they have had **pregnances**, **rapid weight gain**, and/or **growth spurts**.

LOOK

Silvery lines or stripes will indicate old stretch marks

Red lines will indicate newer stretch marks

Old stretch marks

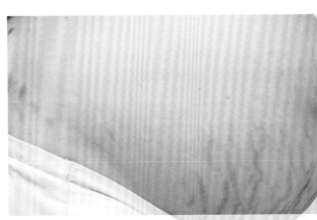

New stretch marks

6

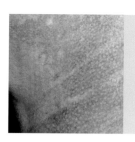

POIKILODERMA OF CIVATTE

LISTEN

Your client may have been given this **diagnosis** before. They often complain of a **red sensitive neck**, or that they have **pigmentation on the sides of their neck** and a **white or pale area under the chin.**

LOOK

Hyperpigmentation with a rash (pinkness)

Little spots of **hypopigmentation** on the **sides of the neck and lower front**, sometimes extended onto the décolleté

Fine visible **blood vessels**

Sometimes mistakenly **attributed to perfumes**

TOUCH

You will feel **roughness** and a **slight bumpiness** of the surface.

7

RASHES

LISTEN

Your client may say that they are reacting to some **chemical** that has initiated an **immune response** by their body. Ask about a **history of allergies.**

LOOK

You will usually see **red, sensitive skin**, possibly with **raised bumps**, **rashes** and **scaly areas**.

67

Occasionally, a client may develop a reaction to a cosmetic product. If the product contains vitamin A then please check whether the client actually has developed a retinoid reaction. This reaction occurs in the early stages of using a vitamin A cream, and appears to be an allergy. However, one cannot be allergic to vitamin A. Dry rashes and even acne breakouts will stop if one stops using the product and then slowly re-introduces it in tiny amounts at a time. Eventually the client who has had a retinoid reaction will be able to use vitamin A every day in strong concentrations. People with retinoid reactions do not need cortisone. The skin has been deficient of vitamin A and vitamin A receptors for too long, and when vitamin A is applied in a moderate dose, it becomes a chemical irritant because it cannot enter the cells. As one introduces vitamin A, the cells start to produce more receptors and the vitamin A enters the cells and does not irritate the skin.

3 SKIN GROUPS

5 SKIN TYPES

7 SKIN CONDITIONS

LEVEL 4.

INTERPRETATION

ACTION PLAN
Ingredients and treatments selector

HOW TO USE THE INTERPRETATION CHART

You now **know a lot** about your client – their **major concern**, **Skin Group**, **Skin Type** and **Skin Condition**. This document will help you to **chart** that **information** and provide a place for you to make notes.

1   **Choose** the appropriate Interpretation Chart **by Skin Group**.

2   **Choose** the appropriate column **by Skin Type**.

3   **Choose** the relevant **Skin Conditions**.

4   **Tick** the relevant **conditions**.

5   **Make your notes** on the right hand side.

6   **Attach** to your **Client Record**.

Go to www.skinscienceauthority.com to download your free copy of these interpretation charts.

GROUP A — PALE, LIGHT SKINS

SKIN CONDITIONS		1 NORMAL SKIN	2 COMBINATION SKIN	3 DRY SKIN	4 OILY SKIN	5 RED/ SENSITIVE SKIN
PHOTO-AGEING	Mild					
	Moderate					
	Severe					
ACNE	Moderate					
	Severe					
PIGMENTATION	Solar					
	Hormonal/Melasma					
	Post-traumatic Inflammatory					
ROSACEA						
SURFACE IRREGULARITIES	Normal Moles					
	Abnormal Moles					
	Scars – Acne					
	Scars – Trauma					
	Scars – Keloid					
	Stretch marks – Old					
	Stretch marks – New					
POIKILODERMA OF CIVATTE						
RASHES						

NAME:

COMMENTS:

71

LIGHT BROWN SKINS

SKIN CONDITIONS

SKIN TYPE:

		1 NORMAL SKIN	2 COMBINATION SKIN	3 DRY SKIN	4 OILY SKIN	5 RED/ SENSITIVE SKIN
PHOTO-AGEING	Mild					
	Moderate					
	Severe					
ACNE	Moderate					
	Severe					
PIGMENTATION	Solar					
	Hormonal/Melasma					
	Post-traumatic Inflammatory					
ROSACEA						
SURFACE IRREGULARITIES	Normal Moles					
	Abnormal Moles					
	Scars – Acne					
	Scars – Trauma					
	Scars – Keloid					
	Stretch marks – Old					
	Stretch marks – New					
POIKILODERMA OF CIVATTE						
RASHES						

NAME:

COMMENTS:

DARK SKINS

SKIN CONDITIONS		SKIN TYPE:				
		1 NORMAL SKIN	2 COMBINATION SKIN	3 DRY SKIN	4 OILY SKIN	5 RED/ SENSITIVE SKIN
PHOTO-AGEING	Mild					
	Moderate					
	Severe					
ACNE	Moderate					
	Severe					
PIGMENTATION	Solar					
	Hormonal/Melasma					
	Post-traumatic Inflammatory					
ROSACEA						
SURFACE IRREGULARITIES	Normal Moles					
	Abnormal Moles					
	Scars – Acne					
	Scars – Trauma					
	Scars – Keloid					
	Stretch marks – Old					
	Stretch marks – New					
POIKILODERMA OF CIVATTE						
RASHES						

NAME:

COMMENTS:

3 SKIN GROUPS

5 SKIN TYPES

7 SKIN CONDITIONS

INTERPRETATION

LEVEL 5

ACTION PLAN
Ingredients
and treatments selector

HOW TO USE THE ACTION PLAN

You are almost at the **end** of your **Skin Analysis journey** with your client now.

They are probably eager to hear **what they can do** to best take care of the skin they have, and improve the **Skin Conditions** that they came to see you about. You are going to use the **Ingredients and Treatments Selector** to choose the **appropriate plan** for your client.

HOME TREATMENTS

- **Topical creams, gels and ointments**

- **Supplements**

- **Cosmetic Needling**

- **Gentle Peels**

- **Lifestyle changes**

- **Sunsense**

- **Cleansing**

PROFESSIONAL TREATMENTS

- **Peels**

- **Needling**

HOME TREATMENTS

TOPICAL CREAMS, GELS AND OINTMENTS

The Ingredients & Treatments Selector will tell you which ingredients are important for your client. It's up to you to find products that match the client's needs. Your client may need to be shown how to mix products into a 'cocktail' that best suits them.

SUPPLEMENTS

The Ingredients & Treatments Selector will also help you here. Don't forget that you can download a paper by Dr. Des on the subject of supplements at www.skinscienceauthority.com

COSMETIC NEEDLING

If your client wants to do Needling and it is appropriate for their Skin Conditions, you may have to show them how to use the roller properly.

GENTLE PEELS

Discuss this in depth with your client.

LIFESTYLE CHANGES

Trying to include the selected Ingredients in a diet will always be beneficial. Some Skin Conditions require specific dietary changes. Regular exercise helps to keep skin young and healthy.

SUNSENSE

Each Skin Group needs a slightly different approach to skin care while in the sun. See the section on Sunsense.

CLEANSING

Each Skin Type requires a different approach to cleansing. See the section on Skin Types.

PROFESSIONAL TREATMENTS

Discuss these with your client. Your training will tell you whether or not a person is a candidate for a series of treatments. Be sensitive about budget issues.

HOW TO USE THE INGREDIENTS AND TREATMENTS SELECTOR

We designed this **Selector** so that you can take the information you charted on the **Interpretation Chart** and put it to practical use in designing an **Action Plan**.

On the left-hand side, you will see Skin Groups, Skin Types and Skin Conditions. Each **coloured column** represents an **ingredient** that Dr Des suggests you use in the treatment of your client's skin.

It's easy to go down the **left-hand column** and **circle the relevant Skin Group, Skin Type** and **Skin Conditions of your client**, and then **go across the rows to place the crosses in each ingredient** that shows up. The default recommendations are ghosted but you are always the person who decides on the need in the end.

At the **end of the process** you will have the **number of Indicators** for each ingredient for your client's skin.

The **more Indicators** you have for an ingredient, the **more important** it is that your client should include this ingredient in their **skin care routine**. If you need to tailor your **Action Plan** to suit your **client's budget**, then this will help you to **prioritise** your advice. The **Ingredient** with the most Indicators is the one you should **focus on first**.

We've included an example **Selector** and **Action Plan**, so you can see how it's done.

Each Ingredient and **Treatment** in the Selector plays an **important role**, but some are more important than others. **Vitamin A** can **NEVER** be ignored.

 Go to www.skinscienceauthority.com to download your free copy of this Selector.

INGREDIENTS & TREATMENTS SELECTOR:

	VITAMIN A	VITAMIN C	PEPTIDES	HYALUR-ONIC ACID	ANTI-OXIDANTS	MOISTURE FACTORS	ALPHA HYDROXY ACIDS	PEELS	SKIN NEEDLING
SKIN GROUPS									
Group A	✓	✓			✓				✓
Group B	✓	✓			✓				✓
Group C	✓	✓			✓				✓
SKIN TYPES									
Type Normal	✓	✓			✓		✓		✓
Type Dry	✓	✓		✓		✓	✓		✓
Type Oily	✓	✓					✓		✓
Type Combination	✓	✓				✓	✓		✓
Type Red / Sensitive	✓	✓			✓				✓
SKIN CONDITIONS									
PHOTO-AGEING									
Freckles	✓	✓	✓		✓		✓		✓
Pigmentary Blemishes	✓	✓	✓		✓		✓		✓
Fine Wrinkles	✓	✓	✓	✓	✓	✓			✓
Smile Lines	✓	✓	✓	✓	✓	✓			✓
Dry, Ashen Skin	✓	✓		✓	✓	✓	✓		
Uneven Skin Colour	✓	✓	✓		✓	✓	✓	✓	✓
Brown Patches	✓	✓	✓		✓		✓		✓
Deep Static Wrinkles	✓	✓	✓	✓	✓	✓			✓
Easy Bruising		✓	✓	✓					
Elastosis	✓	✓	✓	✓	✓				✓
Laxity	✓	✓	✓	✓	✓		✓	✓	✓
Roughness	✓	✓		✓	✓	✓	✓		
SUB-TOTAL									

INGREDIENTS & TREATMENTS SELECTOR:

	VITAMIN A	VITAMIN C	PEPTIDES	HYALUR-ONIC ACID	ANTI-OXIDANTS	MOISTURE FACTORS	ALPHA HYDROXY ACIDS	PEELS	SKIN NEEDLING
Poor Circulation	✓	✓			✓	✓			✓
Poor Elastic Recoil	✓	✓	✓	✓	✓	✓			✓
Keratosis	✓				✓	✓		✓	
Skin Cancer	✓				✓	✓			
	URGE YOUR CUSTOMER TO SEE THEIR DOCTOR IMMEDIATELY								
ACNE									
Acne	✓	✓					✓	✓	✓
PIGMENTATION									
Solar	✓	✓	✓		✓		✓		✓
Hormonal	✓	✓	✓		✓				✓
Post-traumatic	✓	✓	✓		✓		✓		✓
ROSACEA									
Rosacea	✓	✓			✓	✓	✓	✓	✓
SURFACE IRREGULARITIES									
Abnormal Moles	URGE YOUR CUSTOMER TO SEE THEIR DOCTOR IMMEDIATELY								
Scars									
Scars – Acne	✓		✓				✓	✓	✓
Scars – Trauma	✓	✓	✓				✓		✓
Scars – Keloid	✓		✓						✓
Stretch Marks	✓	✓	✓			✓			✓
POIKILODERMA OF CIVATTE									
Poikiloderma	✓	✓	✓		✓				✓
RASHES									
Allergies	✓				✓				
Eczema/Atopy	✓				✓	✓			
TOTAL									

GROUP A

These are potentially the most sun-damaged skins that you will see. They are depleted in vitamin A, vitamin C, antioxidants and hyaluronic acid. They suffer from damage to collagen, so one would recommend peptides. Low doses of Alpha or beta hydroxy acids may also be beneficial. Later on, peeling may play a good role.

GROUP B

These skins have a tendency for less sun damage, but occasionally one sees the worst photo-ageing so these people also need vitamin A, vitamin C and antioxidants. Alpha and beta hydroxy acids are useful as well as hyaluronic acid and peptides. If they have dry skin, which is common, then they need specific moisturising factors as well. Peeling is of value at the right time.

GROUP C

You will generally see much less sun damage in these skins. They are able to protect their vitamin A, vitamin C and antioxidants very well, which is why they show so little photo-ageing. However, they do get superficial damage and also deep Infra-red light damage which is why they need antioxidants, vitamin C and vitamin A. Hyaluronic acid may be of value if there is significant sun damage. Peptides, are less required.

82

SUNSENSE PLANS

SUNSENSE PLAN FOR GROUP A

NATURAL PROTECTION FROM UVB	NATURAL PROTECTION FROM UVA	PROTECTION REQUIRED	FREQUENCY WHILE IN THE SUN	UNPROTECTED DURATION IN SUN
Very little – SPF 2 at most	None	Minimum SPF15-20 with 5*UVA or equivalent	Apply every 90-120 minutes	No more than 10 minutes – 5 minutes to get vitamin D levels

SUNSENSE PLAN FOR GROUP B

NATURAL PROTECTION FROM UVB	NATURAL PROTECTION FROM UVA	PROTECTION REQUIRED	FREQUENCY WHILE IN THE SUN	UNPROTECTED DURATION IN SUN
SPF 3-4	2*	Minimum SPF15-20 with 5*UVA or equivalent	Apply every 90-120 minutes	No more than 20-30 minutes – 20 minutes to get vitamin D levels

SUNSENSE PLAN FOR GROUP C

NATURAL PROTECTION FROM UVB	NATURAL PROTECTION FROM UVA	PROTECTION REQUIRED	FREQUENCY WHILE IN THE SUN	UNPROTECTED DURATION IN SUN
SPF 8-14	3*	Minimum SPF10-15 with 5*UVA or equivalent	Apply every 90-120 minutes	No more than 30-40 minutes – 30 minutes to get vitamin D levels

SKIN TYPES

NORMAL SKIN

COMBINATION SKIN

DRY SKIN

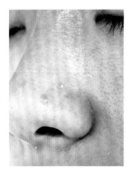

OILY SKIN

RED / SENSITIVE SKIN

These need vitamin A, vitamin C and antioxidants as basic protection. Alpha and beta hydroxy acids become important in older normal skins. As you go down the Selector page, you will identify the specific needs for hyaluronic acid, peptides and moisturising factors. Do not use soap more than once a day, and generally only if you use make-up, or have surface grime.

Of all the Skin Types we see, this is the most common. They need vitamin A in controlled doses with vitamin C and antioxidants. Do not use soap more than once a day, and generally only if you use make-up, or have surface grime.

These skins need moisturising based on natural moisturising factors. Hyaluronic acid is important, but remember they do need to use a superficial epidermal roller to enhance its effectiveness. Vitamin A must be given carefully, but vitamin C and antioxidants are very important. Try to avoid all soaps - use cream-based cleansers.

This can be can be difficult skin to treat. You must gradually achieve high levels of vitamin A to control excessive sebum production. Vitamin C and antioxidants are always important to protect oily skin. Alpha and beta hydroxy acids are also useful. Peeling may also be of help. Be careful not to wash your face too often. Avoid harsh foaming gel cleansers. Paradoxically, harsh cleansing will incite the sebaceous glands to produce more oil. Cleanse your skin only once per day with a gentle cleanser, preferably in the evening to remove surface grime.

These are generally Group A skins. They have significant dilation of the fine capillaries in their skin and are generally photo-sensitive. Vitamin C and antioxidants are very important to help develop the vascular supporting collagen. Vitamin A must be started very gently and used progressively. Sensitive type skins also tend to be in Group A. Their immune system needs boosting and vitamin A is an important method of doing that. They may be ultra-sensitive to it and it should be used only intermittently in the beginning. Avoid all soap – the best way to clean this skin is by gentle rubbing with fingers and water. Removal of make-up with gentle products is recommended.

SKIN CONDITIONS – TREATMENTS

PHOTO-AGEING

FRECKLES

Freckles are one of the first signs of sun damage. They can be treated with Vitamin A and C, peptides, Anti-oxidants, alpha and beta hydroxy acids and needling. Use sun protection to avoid getting more.

PIGMENTARY BLEMISHES

Always push up levels of vitamin A and vitamin C and antioxidants to minimise formation of pigmentation. Alpha hydroxy acids are also useful in treatment.

FINE WRINKLES

You need to treat the damaged collagen that this condition represents with vitamin A, vitamin C, antioxidants, peptides, and alpha and beta hydroxy acids. Hyaluronic acid is also important. Peels are often indicated to smoothen a rough stratum corneum.

SMILE LINES

Smile lines develop over time due to muscle activity but are aggravated by sun damage. They should be treated with vitamins A and C, peptides as well as hyaluronic acid, anti-oxidants and moisture factors. Needling should make a difference to smile lines.

DRY, ASHEN SKIN

You should keep vitamin A levels low while you address the moisture problems with vitamin C and antioxidants, alpha and beta hydroxy acids, natural moisturising factors and hyaluronic acid.

UNEVEN SKIN COLOUR

This is also a sign of vitamin A deficiency so we need to address this primarily with vitamin A, vitamin C and other antioxidants. Alpha hydroxy acids may be useful and in Skin Group A and B, peeling can help. There are certain products designed specially to address melanin disorders.

BROWN PATCHES

Always push up levels of vitamin A and vitamin C and antioxidants to minimise formation of pigmentation. Alpha hydroxy acids are also useful in treatment.

DEEP STATIC WRINKLES

You need to treat the damaged collagen that this condition represents with vitamin A, vitamin C, antioxidants, peptides, and alpha and beta hydroxy acids. Hyaluronic acid is also important. Peels are often indicated to smoothen a rough stratum corneum.

EASY BRUISING

This is generally seen in older people with significant photo-ageing. The main cause is loss of hyaluronic acid which normally "cushions" the tissues. It can be built up with special forms of topical hyaluronic acid, vitamin A and vitamin C. Vitamin C helps to support collagens for the blood vessels. Vitamin A is the main stimulator of the production of hyaluronic acid.

ELASTOSIS

This is usually due to sun damage and is called actinic elastosis. In the early stages one may be able to see white-yellowish tiny nodules in the dermis of the neck or lower eyelids of sun damaged skin. With increased sun damage one may see the fissured yellow rigid skin at the back of the neck for example. The best treatment is intense sunscreens that cover UV as well as infrared rays. Then topically vitamin A enhanced with 0.1 to 0.2 mm skin needling to enhance activity. Oral vitamin A will improve sun resistance. Finally skin needling with 1.0 needles offers the best chance for improvement.

LAXITY

One has to strengthen the web of collagen to pull the skin tighter. Increased elastin deposition is also required and these are best stimulated by vitamin A and C with selected peptides. Skin needling with 1.0 mm long needles is probably the most effective way to treat laxity.

ROUGHNESS

Roughness of the skin caused by sun damage should be treated with vitamins A and C as well as hyaluronic acid, anti-oxidants and moisture factors.

POOR CIRCULATION

Vitamin A will reverse the impaired circulation from sun damage to some degree, and antioxidants are essential. Alpha and beta hydroxy acids are also important.

POOR ELASTIC RECOIL

This condition means there has been a loss of collagen and elastin with less glycoseaminoglycans, so we need vitamin A, vitamin C, antioxidants, peptides to promote structural fibres like collagen and elastin and also hyaluronic acid.

KERATOSIS

This indicates severe sun damage and your client needs vitamin A, developing up to the highest doses. Vitamin C and antioxidants are good for general protection. Repeated mild dose peeling can be a useful treatment for these people.

SKIN CANCER

If you suspect that your client has skin cancer, they should be referred to their doctor or dermatologist. You can suggest vitamins and antioxidants for general skincare. **Urge your customer to see their doctor immediately.**

SKIN CONDITIONS – TREATMENTS (CONTD.)

ACNE

MILD, MODERATE AND SEVERE

These conditions all need more or less the same basic treatment. Vitamin A is always an important part of the control. Go to higher doses if acne persists. Vitamin C has been shown to reduce acne. There may be hydration problems at the same time as the acne occurs, so you can recommend mild cleansing only once a day with a gentle cleanser and use water and fingers otherwise. Alpha and beta hydroxy acids can be very useful. Numerous added products exist for persistent acne. Many cases respond to the simple addition of vitamin A.

PIGMENTATION

SOLAR PIGMENTATION

Always push up levels of vitamin A and vitamin C and antioxidants to minimise formation of pigmentation. Alpha hydroxy acids are also useful in treatment.

HORMONAL PIGMENTATION

This is extremely difficult to treat and that is why it is important to define it properly. Basic skin care of vitamin A, C and antioxidants are essential. There are specific products on the market that may help, but generally this condition relapses.

POST-TRAUMATIC PIGMENTATION

Post-traumatic/inflammatory Pigmentation: In people with darker skins they can develop pigmentation after injuring the skin. If they get a laceration then the skin surrounding the scar can become hyper-pigmented. Many people who get acne also get darker pigmentation not only in the acne scars themselves but often in the surrounding area that was inflamed. In many cases, people get pigmented areas after an abrasion of the skin and we can even see darker pigmentation in areas where skin rubs together without any inflammation at all. Some people have had rashes and this has been followed by deeper pigmentation. We only know that for some reason the melanocytes have been stimulated to make melanin but treatment is difficult. In some cases the damage results in iron from blood being deposited into the skin and this has a blue-grey appearance rather than brown. This is extremely difficult to treat. I recommend also medical skin needling with a roller where possible. If needling is done with mechanical devices it must be done very lightly otherwise one may aggravate the pigmentation.

ROSACEA

This very debilitating condition starts off with simple redness of the cheeks, chins and forehead but increases in severity with eruption of acne-like lesions and may end up with rhynophyma and one wants to avoid that by early treatment. I have found the best success I know of by treating the skin with an oil of vitamin A, C and E in high doses and then combining that with TCA or Lactic acid based creams in low concentration that are applied to the area for only ten minutes and repeated weekly for a total of six weeks. Independent research on 30 women and men showed that 80% of cases were treated in four weeks and 100% by six weeks. Supplementary treatments may be required after a year or two.

SURFACE IRREGULARITIES

ABNORMAL MOLES

Urge your customer to see their doctor immediately.

SCARS – ACNE, TRAUMA, KELOID

Established scars should be treated with vitamin A, vitamin C, antioxidants and peptides to promote healthier collagen deposition. Medical skin needling makes an enormous difference.

STRETCH MARKS

These need the highest tolerable levels of vitamin A and vitamin C and antioxidants as a basic treatment. Peptides also help, but the best treatment is medical skin needling once the skin is adapted to high levels of vitamin A. Skin needling with 1.0 or even 3.0 done lightly is probably the most reliable way to treat stretch marks. However, prevention is better by keeping the skin rich in vitamin A especially before pregnancy.

POIKILODERMA OF CIVATTE

It is difficult to treat the pigmentation, redness and elastosis, but you can use vitamin A, vitamin C and antioxidants with peptides for protracted periods in order to see improvements. Skin needling with 1.0 mm needles preferably with a roller will reduce the vascularity and also lighten the pigmentation and smoothen out the neck skin. Several treatments are recommended at short intervals.

RASHES

ALLERGIES, ECZEMA AND ATOPY

These are common, and represent a problem with the outer layer of skin. Vitamin A is particularly useful for re-establishing the outer layer so should always play a part. It is not necessary to use very high levels. Vitamin C and Antioxidants also very important to protect skin. Always keep treatment as simple as possible.

"Do not forget to discover if your client is already using a vitamin A or antioxidant topical cream and/or supplements. This will affect your recommendation for home treatments, professional treatments, and supplements."

CUSTOMER RECORD CARD COVER

Your customer record card template looks similar to this.

CUSTOMER DETAILS

Name:

Age:

Sex:

Date of Skin Analysis:

Your customer's photographs go here.

Full frontal

Left side

Right side

CUSTOMER'S MAJOR CONCERN

SKIN GROUP

SKIN TYPE

SKIN CONDITIONS

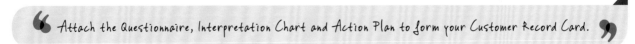
Use the indicators from the Ingredients & Treatments Selector, and fill in below.

INGREDIENTS & TREATMENTS SELECTED:

	VITAMIN A	VITAMIN C	PEPTIDES	HYALUR-ONIC ACID	ANTI-OXIDANTS	MOISTURE FACTORS	ALPHA HYDROXY ACIDS	PEELS	SKIN NEEDLING
INDICATORS									

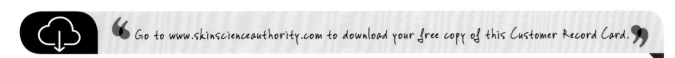
Attach the Questionnaire, Interpretation Chart and Action Plan to form your Customer Record Card.

Go to www.skinscienceauthority.com to download your free copy of this Customer Record Card.

SUMMARY

"We hope that by using your Skin Analysis Practical Guide you will get sophisticated information delivered in a simple way to help you understand your client's skin and how best to treat it.

We have focussed on understanding first of all, your clients' **Skin Group** to assess their resistance to sun damage. This will guide you on your sensible sun protection plan for your client to save their skin, but still protect their health by promoting vitamin D formation.

From your knowledge of the detailed anatomy of the skin, you will understand your clients' **Skin Type**, and you'll get an idea of the functioning of the keratinocytes of the skin that determine the production of natural moisturising factors that keep skin normal and prevent dryness. You also get an idea of the health of the stratum corneum that, when impaired, causes red sensitive skin. You will see the function of the sebaceous glands and whether they are over producing or under-producing sebum. On the other hand, malfunctioning keratinocytes and an impaired stratum corneum together with malfunctioning sebaceous glands causes dry Skin Conditions and sensitivities. Understanding how the melanocyte causes pigmentation, and where the pigmentation is deposited, helps you treat your clients' skin.

Alterations in the activity of the major cells of the skin determine the **Skin Conditions**. Sunlight, both visible in the blue violet and ultraviolet as well as the damaging component of infra-red make changes to all the cells in the epidermis as well as the deeper compartments of skin. They are responsible for all the manifestations of photo-ageing. The production and destruction of deep structural proteins of collagen and elastin, as well as the glycoseaminoglycan (hyaluronic acid) gel that fills out the skin, are changed by light.

Malfunction of the stratum corneum and damage to blood vessels in the dermis initiate sensitive and red skin.

Changes in the stratum corneum and the follicles and sebaceous glands are responsible for acne.

Alterations in the melanocytes i.e. in how it gets stimulated, and how pigment gets formed and distributed, determines pigmentary blemishes.

We have stressed that your client is going to tell you what the problem is and your eyes and fingers are going to discover the possibilities, and finally machines may confirm your diagnosis.

When you have used our **Skin Analysis Funnel** efficiently you will find it easier to work out a programme for your client."

93

FOLLOW UP

If you have recommended a regimen for a client, then contact them the next day or suggest that they should report back to you.

"REGULAR FOLLOW UP IS CRITICAL "

If you have recommended a professional treatment then it is good to contact them the next day.

- By telephone or text the next day

- Enquire as to appearance and comfort

- Your client will appreciate your thoughtfulness

- Problem solving, if necessary, must be done by you

- Keep in touch over the following weeks if the treatment requires it

KEY FACTS

Some of the documents available at www.skinscienceauthority.com (these may vary from time to time)

Vitamin A

Vitamin B

Vitamin C

Vitamin D

Peptides

Hyaluronic Acid

Alpha & Beta
Hydroxy Acids

Supplements
for Skin

Peels

Needling

Exfoliation

Sun Care

TEMPLATES

The templates available at www.skinscienceauthority.com

Questionnaire

Interpretation
Chart

Ingredients
Selector

Customer
Record Card

❝ Dr Des Fernandes shares some KEY FACTS with you, the readers of Skin Analysis, A Practical Guide. These documents are available to download when you go to www.skinscienceauthority.com. The templates are available when you log in with the registration number that you will find on the back cover of this book. ❞

❝ You will also find an opportunity to subscribe to the SKIN ANALYSIS WEB TOOL if you want to add a digital approach to your business. This app will take you through the Skin Analysis Funnel, step by step, with videos, pictures and documents to help you all the way through. Our app will give you the next best thing to having Dr Des in the room with you during a consultation. ❞

BIBLIOGRAPHY

1   Rampen, F.H. and P.E. de Wit, Racial differences in mole proneness. Acta Derm Venereol, 1989. 69(3): p. 234-6.

2   Abdel-Malek, Z., et al., Analysis of the UV-induced melanogenesis and growth arrest of human melanocytes. Pigment Cell Res, 1994. 7(5): p. 326-32.

3   Eller, M.S., K. Ostrom, and B.A. Gilchrest, DNA damage enhances melanogenesis. Proc Natl Acad Sci U S A, 1996. 93(3): p. 1087-92.

4   Cripps, D.J., Natural and artificial photoprotection. J Invest Dermatol, 1981. 77(1): p. 154-7.

5   Welgus, H.G. and G.P. Stricklin, Human skin fibroblast collagenase inhibitor. Comparative studies in human connective tissues, serum, and amniotic fluid. J Biol Chem, 1983. 258(20): p. 12259-64.

6   Welgus, H.G., et al., Human skin fibroblast collagenase: interaction with substrate and inhibitor. Coll Relat Res, 1985. 5(2): p. 167-79.

7   Ditre, C.M., et al., Effects of alpha-hydroxy acids on photoaged skin: a pilot clinical, histologic, and ultrastructural study. J Am Acad Dermatol, 1996. 34(2 Pt 1): p. 187-95.

8   Sakai, S., et al., N-methyl-L-serine stimulates hyaluronan production in human skin fibroblasts. Skin Pharmacol Appl Skin Physiol, 1999. 12(5): p. 276-83.

9   Sakai, S., et al., Hyaluronan exists in the normal stratum corneum. J Invest Dermatol, 2000. 114(6): p. 1184-7.

10 Sayo, T., S. Sakai, and S. Inoue, Synergistic effect of N-acetylglucosamine and retinoids on hyaluronan production in human keratinocytes. Skin Pharmacol Physiol, 2004. 17(2): p. 77-83.

11   Swweath, R.J. and D.C. Mangham, The normal structure and function of CD44 and its role in neoplasia. Mol Pathol, 1998. 51(4): p. 191-200.

12   Lee, S.E., et al., Stimulation of epidermal calcium gradient loss increases the expression of hyaluronan and CD44 in mouse skin. Clin Exp Dermatol, 2009.

13   King, I.A., Increased epidermal hyaluronic acid synthesis caused by four retinoids. Br J Dermatol, 1984. 110(5): p. 607-8.

14   Kaya, G., et al., Hyaluronate fragments reverse skin atrophy by a CD44-dependent mechanism. PLoS Med, 2006. 3(12): p. e493.

15   Calikoglu, E., et al., UVA and UVB decrease the expression of CD44 and hyaluronate in mouse epidermis, which is counteracted by topical retinoids. Photochem Photobiol, 2006. 82(5): p. 1342-1347.

16   K. R. Smith* and D. M. Thiboutot1,*,†, Sebaceous gland lipids: friend or foe? Jake Gittlen Cancer Research Foundation* and Department of Dermatology,† Pennsylvania State University College of Medicine, Hershey, PA 17033

17   Green C, Orchard G, Cerio R, Hawk JL. A clinicopathological study of the effects of topical retinyl propionate cream in skin photo-ageing. Clin Exp Dermatol. 1998;23(4):162-7.

18   Fernandes DB. Evolution of Cosmeceuticals and Their Application to Skin Disorders, Including Aging and Blemishes. Dermatological and Cosmeceutical Development: Absorption Efficacy and Toxicity. Edited by Kenneth A Walters, Michael S. Roberts2007. p. 45-60.

19   Baumann L. Skin aging and its treatment. J Pathol. 2007;211(2): 241-51.

20   Sayo, Saurat JH. Skin, sun, and vitamin A: from aging to cancer. J Dermatol. 2001;28(11):595-8.

21   Love WK, Berletch JB, Andrews LG, Tollefsbol TO. Epigenetic regulation of telomerase in retinoid-induced differentiation of human leukemia cells. Int J Oncol. 2008;32(3):625-31.

Jennie and Des wish you enjoyment
in discovering how easy it is to
analyse your clients' skins and
build sensible skin care regimens.

ABOUT THE AUTHORS

After qualifying M.B.; B.Ch. at the Witwatersrand University, **Des Fernandes** became a fellow of the Royal College of Surgeons at Edinburgh. Following his training as a Cardiac Surgeon with Prof Christiaan Barnard, he started specialising in Plastic Surgery. Along with his sister Valerie Carstens, he is a co-founder of a global skin care company.

Jennifer Munro is an author and ex Creative Director in the advertising industry. Her long-term friendship with Des has made it possible for her to interpret his most important messages for people who want to better understand their skins, and put them into as simple as format as possible.

As co-authors, we want you to use this book to simplify your analysis of skin, and help you to avoid getting bogged down in unnecessary detail. If you feel you would like a more inter-active digital experience, please look out for our software version.